Sunrise, Sunset

LYRICS BY **Sheldon Harnick** ~ MUSIC BY **Jerry Bock**

ILLUSTRATED BY **Ian Schoenherr**

HarperCollinsPublishers

For Charlotte and Sam

Is this the little girl I carried?
Is this the little boy at play?

When did she get to be a beauty?
When did he grow to be so tall?

Wasn't it yesterday

when they were small?

Sunrise, sunset,
Sunrise, sunset,
Swiftly flow the days;

Seedlings turn overnight to sunflow'rs,

Blossoming even as we gaze.

Sunrise, sunset,
Sunrise, sunset,
Swiftly fly the years;

One season following another,

Laden with happiness and tears.

Now is the little boy a bridegroom,
Now is the little girl a bride.

Under the canopy I see them,
Side by side.

Place the gold ring around her finger,
Share the sweet wine and break the glass;
Soon the full circle will have come to pass.

Sunrise, sunset,
Sunrise, sunset,
Swiftly flow the days;

Seedlings turn overnight to sunflow'rs,
Blossoming even as we gaze.

Sunrise, sunset,
    Sunrise, sunset,
        Swiftly fly the years;

One season following another,
    Laden with happiness and tears.

Sunrise, Sunset • Text and music © 1964, renewed 1992, by Mayerling Productions Ltd. and Jerry Bock Enterprises •
Illustrations copyright © 2005 by Ian Schoenherr • Manufactured in China. • All rights reserved. • www.harperchildrens.com
For information address HarperCollins Children's Books, a division of HarperCollins Publishers, 10 East 53rd Street, New
York, NY 10022.

Library of Congress Cataloging-in-Publication Data Harnick, Sheldon. Sunrise, sunset / lyrics by Sheldon Harnick ;
music by Jerry Bock ; illustrated by Ian Schoenherr. — 1st ed.   p.   cm. Summary: An illustrated version of the
well-known song about the passage of time, from the musical "Fiddler on the Roof." ISBN 978-0-06-220582-7
1. Children's songs, English—United States—Texts. [1. Songs.] I. Bock, Jerry. II. Schoenherr, Ian, ill. III. Title.
PZ8.3.H2183Su 2005   2004019104   782.42—dc22   CIP   [E]   AC
Typography by Martha Rago   12 13 14 SCP 10 9 8 7 6 5 4 3 2 1 ❖ First Edition

The illustrations for this book were made with colored pencil, permanent ink, and acrylic paint on Bristol board.